PECULIAR PETS

Treasured Verses

Edited By Debbie Killingworth

First published in Great Britain in 2021 by:

 Young**Writers**® ── Est. 1991 ──

Young Writers
Remus House
Coltsfoot Drive
Peterborough
PE2 9BF
Telephone: 01733 890066
Website: www.youngwriters.co.uk

Printed and bound in the UK by BookPrintingUK
Website: www.bookprintinguk.com
YB0455F

★ FOREWORD ★

Welcome Reader!

Are you ready to discover weird and wonderful creatures that you'd never even dreamed of?

For Young Writers' latest competition we asked primary school pupils to create a Peculiar Pet of their own invention, and then write a poem about it! They rose to the challenge magnificently and the result is this fantastic collection full of creepy critters and amazing animals!

Here at Young Writers our aim is to encourage creativity in children and to inspire a love of the written word, so it's great to get such an amazing response, with some absolutely fantastic poems. Not only have these young authors created imaginative and inventive animals, they've also crafted wonderful poems to showcase their creations and their writing ability. These poems are brimming with inspiration. The slimiest slitherers, the creepiest crawlers and furriest friends are all brought to life in these pages – you can decide for yourself which ones you'd like as a pet!

I'd like to congratulate all the young authors in this anthology, I hope this inspires them to continue with their creative writing.

★

★ CONTENTS ★

Dixons Marchbank Primary School, Bradford

Ibrahim Mahmood (8)	69
Hibba Hassain (8)	70
Tayyibah Munir (8)	71
Abdulaboor Hussain (8)	72
Inaya Hussain (8)	73
Sehr Zafran (8)	74
Musa Mohammad (8)	75
Aayat Hussain (8)	76
Amina Ali (8)	77

Lee Chapel Primary School, Basildon

Akshadha Jacksun (11)	78
Max Huggins (10)	79
Lowalekar (10)	80
Faramade Aderin (10)	81
Veera Pasapula (10)	82

Lenham Primary School, Lenham

Elizabeth Costain (8)	83
Jessica Cushion (9)	84
Skye Jackson (8)	85
Millie Sharp (8)	86
Isabella Young (8)	87
Poppy Storey (8)	88
Riley Carrano (8)	89
Louanna Lambert (8)	90

Litcham School, Litcham

James Casey (9)	91
Ivo Pickard (9)	92
Tristan How (10)	94
Tegan Smith (9)	96
Reece Watts (10)	98
Raphael Westwood (9)	99
James Millward (9)	100
Lyra Bannister (9)	101
Caden Brabant (10)	102
Damian Rees (9)	103

May Pick (9)	104
Katherine Seales (9)	105
Erin Reynolds (9)	106
Martha Wright (9)	107
Faris Matsell (9)	108
Ollie Barron (9)	109
Philippa Elburn (9)	110
Katie Hanson	111
Georgia Moores (9)	112

Melrose At The Ladies College, St Peter Port

Louisa Hardovin-Munro (10)	113
Rea Moore (10)	114
Alexa Stockwell (10)	116
Holly Jones (10)	117
Amelia Willis (10)	118
Caitlin Vidamour (10)	119
Isabelle Guest (10)	120

St Andrew's CE Primary School, Plymouth

Cayde Cummins (7)	121
Tabitha Ryder (7)	122
Molly Pinder (8)	123
George Andrei (8)	124
Iyla Hammond (8)	125
Noah Wallbridge-Willcocks (8)	126
Freddie Colling (7)	127
Catherine Phillips Ebohon (7)	128
Yohan Dean (7)	129
Emily-Rose Trevaskus	130
Amber Loram-Martin (7)	131
Orla Stafford (7)	132
Jacqueson Berry (7)	133
Delphine Marie Edwards (7)	134
Theo Strong (7)	135
Daria Bighiu (7)	136
Rehaan Chatterjee (7)	137
Nathan Ogwu (8)	138
Mia Flynn (8)	139
Audrey Victoria Almirante Biggs (7)	140

THE POEMS

COME ON SLOW COACH

Acrobatic Tortoise

A mazing, exciting, fantastic!

C ome see the marvellous acrobatic tortoise.

R emarkable, unimaginable!

O pen to everyone in the world.

B ored with school, well come see him.

A fraid of coming? Well you'll miss out.

T oo excited, book a ticket now!

I n you go, into the arena.

C hildren screaming, adults shouting.

T o represent the

O ne and only acrobatic tortoise.

R ight, in comes the tortoise ready to battle!

T he tortoise is against the flying zebra.

O n goes the battle.

I ncredible, exciting!

S uddenly the zebra is knocked out.

E veryone goes wild for the amazing acrobatic tortoise!

Joseph Spink (10)

Chellaston Junior School, Chellaston

Cuddling Koala

C uddling koala is a wonderful sight.

U nless you like dragons and reading rats.

D ancing dogs and magic.

D efinitely, love is special, especially to cuddling koalas.

L ove is special for everyone.

I n the night he lies beside me and hugs.

N ight and day he cuddles and hugs.

G ladly when he goes to sleep I kiss him and say goodnight.

K oala, koala, oh how cute you are.

O h, you're extraordinary as a flying dog.

A wonderful sight, hugging everyone.

L ove this pet with all your heart.

A wonderful sight for all of us.

Joel Burns (8)
Chellaston Junior School, Chellaston

Dancing Dog

D ancing Dog is a dog that goes dancing.

A t night you can hear the music.

N ow Max is crunching and munching on his bone.

C uriously at night he walks to the garden and starts dancing.

I always tell Max to go to bed but he just doesn't listen.

N ot always but sometimes he goes to bed at night.

"G ot to do some dancing," he says at 6am in the morning.

D ancing Dog goes dancing every evening, he is obsessed.

O n Mondays Dancing Dog goes dancing with his friends.

G oing dancing makes Dancing Dog hyper for when he comes home.

Riah Hanson (8)
Chellaston Junior School, Chellaston

Deen, My Dancing Deer

My deer is very groovy,
On the dance floor she likes to boogie.

Her name is Deen,
The best dancer you have seen.

She twirls, she spins,
She even beautifully sings.

She dances with her head held high,
Then whirls until she reaches the sky.

Deen's fur is a gentle pink,
But changes colours when her hooves clink.

Revolting vegetables turn into an enormous sweet,
Whenever she sits down to eat.

She is unique, audacious and free,
But Deen chooses to always be with me.

Bhavjot Kaur Dhamrait (10)
Chellaston Junior School, Chellaston

Nickey

Nickey, the half narwhal, half seahorse and half turtle.
She is colourful, clever and so cute.
Nickey spends her time swimming
And learning new tricks like flips and dips.
But Nickey wants a friend, so she got a friend.
Nickey, an outstanding, incredible animal.
Incredible, clever and smart.
Colourful, elegant, half narwhal, half seahorse, half turtle.
She's a kid's best friend.
Everything Nickey does represents her personality.
You have never seen a sea creature as beautiful as Nickey.

Eleanor Ives (8)

Chellaston Junior School, Chellaston

Mousiraffe

My mousiraffe is gentle and calm
And likes to play around the farm.
Up and down the field all morning
Until it's time to stop yawning.
Run to school, don't stop to play,
Luckily he got an A.
Finally lunch, meatballs and pasta, yum, yum,
After dinner, I'm gonna have so much fun.
Run around playing tag.
"Ouch!" He tripped over some dirty rags.
School is marshmallows for dinner,
Dinner, winner!
Bedtime and don't start yawning
Till morning.

Freya Moseley (8)
Chellaston Junior School, Chellaston

Beautiful Beauty

B est peculiar pet ever

E xciting as a party

A mazingly fabulous

U p to no good

T he main thing is that she's a star

I 'm amazed at how blonde she is

F ull of perfectness and joy

U nbelievably cute

L et her shine

B et you don't have a pet like this

E xquisite

A t one with fashion

U nbelievably fabulous

T hat cheeky pet

Y ep, she's really real!

Brooke Carson (8)
Chellaston Junior School, Chellaston

The Giraffe, Village And The Boy

G reat giraffe, what are you doing? You're awakening the village.

I run, walk, skip and jump until I get your attention.

R oaring like a lion I roar, run, rage and scream until I get help.

A nxiously I climb on your back and off we go, flying away.

F lying so high like a real superhero but still the giraffe is

F lying soullessly, nothing will help it be happy.

E agerly I fly and feel like I'm dreaming, a dream that won't end.

Anna Goralczyk (8)
Chellaston Junior School, Chellaston

Flying Dog Facts

F lying Dog is fantastic.

L oving as well, lying on the floor he is,

Y elling for me to stroke him.

I n case you didn't know he's also adorable.

N ice he is, he's always happy and nice.

G nawing on his bone like a good dog.

D oing what he normally does, sitting on my bed.

O n my bed, yes, he loves my bed not his.

G oing on flights together, getting wet in the rain, what a good dog he is.

Dexter Sharpe (8)

Chellaston Junior School, Chellaston

Oh No, Help Me, A Girafasaurus!

Oh no, help me!
This monster is trying to eat me!
Oh no, let's check my phone!
It looks like a girafasaurus, all alone.
My phone is down and I am too!
Uh oh, I have to eat too!
Quickly, I have to escape, the door is blocked
With a giant rock.
Oh no, help me!
This monster has eaten me!
Luckily I have a knife.
Quickly I have to slice!
Yes! Now it's dead.
Now I've won the battle of death.
Goodbye monster, argh!

Isaac Poxon (8)
Chellaston Junior School, Chellaston

Dolawolfcat

D angerously climbs rocks.

O range spotty pumpkin eater.

L ittle tiny claws.

A dorable, acts like an angel.

W onderful in every way.

O ldest age it can live for is 100 years.

L ovely, loving pet.

F air but competitive.

C ute, cuddly, clever and colourful.

A mazing at flips in the water.

T o tame this animal you must take it swimming and teach it lots of tricks.

Caitlin Gardiner (9)

Chellaston Junior School, Chellaston

Flying Dog

F antastic one and only dog that can fly.

L ovely and only dog that can fly.

Y ou would love to have a dog like mine.

I n my house he doesn't like to fly.

N o way, he wouldn't fly outside.

G lamorous city, glamorous dog.

D og that can fly, it's amazing, it takes me to the sky.

O range grass, elegantly my dog starts to fly.

G lamorously my dog takes off with me.

Jessica Fitzpatrick (8)

Chellaston Junior School, Chellaston

Cool Horns

C old he is when he's on his head.

O ver the log he jumps, still on his head.

O ut of their league in his gymnastic class.

L egs are no use for this cool dude.

H ead is all he needs.

O ver the sky he flies, still on his head, I don't know why.

R aging and gaming, still on his head.

N ever ever is he gonna get off his head.

S till, he's my perfect pet.

Braiden Martin (8)

Chellaston Junior School, Chellaston

My Pet Hamster, Fluffy, Cute Dog And Fat Fish

H angs on its bars
A lways in its cage
M unching on food
S pins around in its wheel
T ime to drink
E ating food
R uns around in its cage

D og playing with his friends
O n the grass having fun
G oing for a walk

F at fish
I 'm feeding my fish
S eafood
H aving fish for dinner.

Lily Taylor (7)
Chellaston Junior School, Chellaston

Singing Flamingo

F lapping in the breeze.

L oving her forever.

A nd dancing and singing, oh I love her.

"M ore, more, more!" I shout as she plays to me.

I n the garden we sing and play.

N ot caring about the noise we dance elegantly.

G oing to my bed now, see you in the morning.

O n my bed I watch her dance and sing in the moonlight.

Lila Fisher (8)
Chellaston Junior School, Chellaston

Frosty

F reezes a lot when he is bad, like when he is very bad!

R oasts himself in the sun and then he defrosts himself.

O ften he just sleeps on the sofa, sometimes for two hours.

S ighs when humans argue because they wake him up.

T akes all of our food and then we have no food to eat.

Y awns a lot because he is tired because he flies all the time.

Charlotte Goodman (8)
Chellaston Junior School, Chellaston

Rainbow In The Sky

R aining rainbow in the marvellous sky.

A dorable white clouds shimmering in the sky.

I ncredible creature, it had a bunny ear.

N aughty pet had 'stinked' up the room.

B oom! Crack! Bad pet. Splat! Mud in the house.

O ur flying pet, oh that is amazing.

W ait for me, I will go and get my flying car.

Emilia Limbert (7)
Chellaston Junior School, Chellaston

The Mysterious Snap Shell

The night that had light was when Snap Shell woke up.
He loved the humans' food
But the humans hated him for eating all the food.
He was alone, no friends, no family, all alone.
But he loved his mysterious apprentice
And Halloween 'cause everyone thought he was a kid
But he was a monster who lived in the forest,
In a cave with a bed.

Pavle Radojcic (8)
Chellaston Junior School, Chellaston

Lola Unicorn

L azy, little feet.
O range, scaly body.
L ong, beautiful horn.
A mazing, light wings.

U nique, sassy, colourful face.
N ice, beautiful wings.
I ncredibly strong feet.
C ute, little teeth.
O pen, bright wings.
R ough, hard feet.
N ice duck body.

Amiley Russell (8)
Chellaston Junior School, Chellaston

Cutey Koala

C urious, climbing trees.
U ltra shiny scales.
T reetop expert.
E ars that can hear miles away.
Y ummy leaves.

K ind, caring creature.
O beying everyone with their rules.
A dorable body with soft grey fur.
L ong tree branches.
A wesome, amazing creature.

Harry-James Simpson (8)
Chellaston Junior School, Chellaston

Sassy Snake!

S assy, oh so sassy.

A lways getting her own way.

S ass, sass and more sass.

S assy, please stop being sassy.

Y ou need to stop.

S assy, please!

N o more of this nonsense

A nd stop saying 'no'!

K icking off for no reason.

E ven after dinner!

Alyssia Smith (8)
Chellaston Junior School, Chellaston

Bad Snakes

S nakes slither and are cheeky.

N asty little creatures, they will strangle you.

A re poisonous, you will be squeezed, they will strangle you.

K ill is the best thing to do. Yes kill!

E vil snakes are bad.

S lithery snakes, they are too evil, let's put them in the garbage bin where they belong.

Javier Hibbert (8) &
Chellaston Junior School, Chellaston

Fish Dog

F ast as The Flash.
I t's huge so you can see him anywhere.
S till he's fast so don't be fooled.
H e's really strong, he could lift a building.

D ozing around underwater.
O ne and only dog that can swim.
G oes around zooming past fish.

Isaac Halliday (8)

Chellaston Junior School, Chellaston

Buster The Bouncing Bunny

B ouncing bunny, oh Buster, you're funny.
U p and down you go on the trampoline.
S inging all the way, doing flips and tricks.
T elling yourself to keep on bouncing.
E ven though you are a funny bunny I love you.
R abbit, Buster, whatever you were I would love you.

Jack Chaplin (8)
Chellaston Junior School, Chellaston

Pegutrunk

P eculiar creature.

E ndangered but absolutely brilliant.

G orgeous scaly tail.

U ltra shiny.

T rickster to bad people.

R eally rubbish and dirty llama neck.

U nknown dragon-like tail.

N ice creature to others.

K ind, sharing animal.

Joshua Williams (8)

Chellaston Junior School, Chellaston

Hollie

H opping haphazardly around the garden.
O pening every door because she's the size of a Shetland pony.
L ight as a feather.
L ight brown bunny fur.
I n a massive garden.
E lly, Hollie's best friend, bounces around the garden with her.

Rebecca Reader (8)
Chellaston Junior School, Chellaston

My Super Cool Pet

C ute but bites.

O bservant.

O fficial.

L azy pet.

-

A dorable animal.

-

S cales that are rough.

A gile speed.

U ltra cool.

R ad guy.

U ltra shiny.

S assy person.

Alfie Chambers (8)
Chellaston Junior School, Chellaston

Cat Bus

C at Bus will take you everywhere.
A nd across the hills you'll go.
T hrough the fields and across the tunnel.

B ut close your mouth, you might get a bug.
U nder the bridge, through the mountain.
S o be best friends.

Senem Iridzhan (9)

Chellaston Junior School, Chellaston

Milkshake Milksnake

M iles from here in a different country
I like rodents for breakfast
L oves baths
K ills its prey
S cales white as snow
N ever mean
A lways calm
K arate is my favourite
E verybody loves me

Ellie Townsend (7)
Chellaston Junior School, Chellaston

Bees' Honey

B ees make yummy honey.

U p in the sky.

M ake honey.

B ees can fly high in the sky.

L et it make more honey.

E ek, it stung me!

B e a bee please.

E vie loves bees.

E veryone loves honey.

Advay Mahadevan (7)
Chellaston Junior School, Chellaston

Bourbon

B ackwards walking then hits his head.

O ver the sofa he goes.

U nder the desk he hides.

R olls around like a stupid man.

B acks up then falls over.

O nly attacks things that move.

N o one takes his toys.

Owen Hamlett-Mills (8)

Chellaston Junior School, Chellaston

Lizard

L izard has a long tongue.

I t likes going in his cage.

Z igzag patterns on its back.

A lizard loves getting stroked.

R are lizards are lovely animals.

D en making is a lizard's favourite things to do.

Johan Rana (7)

Chellaston Junior School, Chellaston

Up And Down

The catasarose goes up and down.
Up and down, up and down, up and down,
The catasarose goes up and down,
Eating a building,
Stamping through the city,
Oh no, it's going to eat me now.
I'm in its tummy and I have to escape.

Juno Brooks (8)
Chellaston Junior School, Chellaston

Long Lizard

L ong, long, stretchy tail.
I t likes its food, yum, yum.
Z ing zing, running around.
A n acrobat climbing up the wall.
R unning angrily I do think he likes running.
D igging, well he is now!

Robin Stevenson (8)
Chellaston Junior School, Chellaston

The Rabbit

R un rabbit run.

A snake appeared, rabbit, a snake

B rilliant running rabbit.

B ug, stay away from the rabbit, bug!

I will feed you rabbit.

T illy is the name I chose for you rabbit.

Imogen Strathern (7)

Chellaston Junior School, Chellaston

Unicorn Story

U sually you can smell candyfloss.
N ear the end of the rainbow you see unicorns.
I see rainbow hair.
C an you find it?
O MG! I see a unicorn.
R un to it.
N early there!

Isabella Bramley (7)

Chellaston Junior School, Chellaston

Lissei

L oves climbing tall trees.
I t gets water from juicy leaves.
S leeps in trees.
S its in trees as big as a giraffe.
E ats a lot.
I t loves drinking milk.

Saanvika Ginjupalli (8)
Chellaston Junior School, Chellaston

Dog

D ancing dog is so cute and cuddly. She dances all the time.

O ver-energetic dog is so smart she does tricks all the time.

G ymnastic dog is good at doing tricks all the time.

Isla Stephenson (7)

Chellaston Junior School, Chellaston

Skye

S neaky as a serpent with a red hat.
K ind, caring and loving like a teddy bear.
Y es to all of the fun things I suggest.
E njoys watching me play video games.

Aaron Hickey (8)

Chellaston Junior School, Chellaston

My Daft Donkey

My daft donkey is a very peculiar pet
As he trots around the room doing a hilarious dance.
He sleeps on my bed while I stroke his soft fur.
He is a very funny pet and is also caring.

Lennon Barker (8)
Chellaston Junior School, Chellaston

The Roboelectro Dog And The Human

There were two humans
And then they saw a dog and a den.
It was not an ordinary dog,
It was not a robodog,
It was a roboelectro dog.
The men did not know what to do then.

Dawid Zgrzebnicki (8)
Chellaston Junior School, Chellaston

Rabbit

R abbits are so, so cute.
A re they vegan?
B ut they are so cute.
B ut are you a nice rabbit?
I t's a rabbit
T ime to eat, baby.

Neha Dhanjal (7)
Chellaston Junior School, Chellaston

The Unicorn

U gly, dark unicorn.

N aughty unicorn.

I t loves rainbows.

C ute unicorn.

O h my love.

R ainbow unicorn.

N ew unicorn.

Umayya Ahmed (7)
Chellaston Junior School, Chellaston

Lionbird

L ovely and cute.

I nteresting.

O nly loves me.

N ice pet.

B ird wings.

I love my pet.

R un!

D angerous.

Damla Cizioglu (8)
Chellaston Junior School, Chellaston

Bird

B irdy, calm down, do some yoga or something.
I want you to eat your scrummy dinner.
R emember your times tables ladybugs birdy!
D o your playtime.

Amelia Corbett (7)
Chellaston Junior School, Chellaston

Midesscar

M aniac.

I gnores you.

D umb.

E njoying.

S ensitive.

S caly.

C ool.

A wesome.

R ed rocker.

Logan Hill (8)
Chellaston Junior School, Chellaston

Skyler

S parkly,
K eeping fun in sight.
Y elling and playing.
L ives like a monkey.
E verything is happy.
R ainbow tame turtle.

Niamh Howell (8)
Chellaston Junior School, Chellaston

My Naughty Cat

C at, why have you got a hat?

A lways climbing trees and frightening mice.

T reetops is where he plays video games and his favourite game is Karate Cats.

Lucas Wynne (7)

Chellaston Junior School, Chellaston

Fred The Gerbil

G o on, run!

E xcellent at jumping.

R un as fast as you can.

B ouncing up high.

I ncredible jumper.

L ittle tiny mind.

James Baker (7)

Chellaston Junior School, Chellaston

Birdy, Birdy, Go, Go, Go!

B ird fly so high in the sky.

I n the night the bird had a fright.

R ing-ring Birdy, get the phone.

D ig Birdy, dig so fast, dig Birdy dig!

Layla Lomas (7)

Chellaston Junior School, Chellaston

Big Bear

B ark I like to scratch.
E veryone says I'm big.
A te a fish today, lovely food.
R unning through the forest like a wild animal.

Sienna Waldron (7)
Chellaston Junior School, Chellaston

Clown In My Kitchen

H orrible kitchen mess.

O h no, the clown again.

R un for your life!

S uper clown.

E ek! Super Clown Horse!

Jay J Gilbank (8)
Chellaston Junior School, Chellaston

The Cat

C urly-tailed cat comes and eats your favourite food.

A furry friend who comes to tea.

T oday we will play all night.

Athalia Zvidzo (7)
Chellaston Junior School, Chellaston

Dog

D evious, cute and cuddly.

O bedient, smart, fast and lazy.

G ymnastic when he's running fast doing tricks.

Ted Rodgers (7)

Chellaston Junior School, Chellaston

Dog

The dog is excited to go for a walk
The cat has gone to his friends
The lizard needs feeding
The hamster likes to exercise.

Evie Smith (7)
Chellaston Junior School, Chellaston

Oscar

O nly fights me.
S cared of his sister.
C ute cat.
A te my dinner.
R uns really fast.

Leona Hodges (8)
Chellaston Junior School, Chellaston

Bluey

B lue bunny.
L azy, sparkly and furry.
U nique.
E ats leaves.
Y ears old, he is four.

Oliver Bowler (8)

Chellaston Junior School, Chellaston

The Cat

Cat eat up,
Or you will starve
So eat up good
At night the cat sleeps peacefully
The cat likes drinks.

Mollie Winfield (7)
Chellaston Junior School, Chellaston

Dog

D o you want a bone?
O ver the fence, another dog was there.
G one. The dog came back home.

Jacob Buzalski (7)
Chellaston Junior School, Chellaston

Cat

C uddly, clever creature.
A dorable when hugging.
T erribly scared when stuck in treetops.

Clara Sower (7)

Chellaston Junior School, Chellaston

Dog

D ancing, funny dog.
O ver-excited and adventurous.
G oes on a walk when it's told to.

Laila Attwood-Brady (7)
Chellaston Junior School, Chellaston

Cat

C ute and cuddly and a bit crazy.
A lways having fun.
T akes his time to have his dinner.

Aarav Malhi (7)
Chellaston Junior School, Chellaston

Cat

C razy, lazy, cuddly cat.

A crobatic gymnast.

T ea. Its fur is the colour of tea.

Henry Reader (7)
Chellaston Junior School, Chellaston

Dog

D evious, dancing dog.
O verpowered, outraged.
G olden, guilty, it's a guard.

Harry Poxon (7)
Chellaston Junior School, Chellaston

The Cat

C ute cat in a tall tree.
A strange dog hurt you, Cat.
T hat cat is falling.

Henry McCristol (7)
Chellaston Junior School, Chellaston

Cat

C ute, creative, cuddly.
A crobatic when landing.
T all when landing.

Elijah Hancock (7)
Chellaston Junior School, Chellaston

My Dog

D og, stop it!
O ops, I fell.
G rowls. Don't be sick!

Oliver Wilson (7)

Chellaston Junior School, Chellaston

YoungWriters Est. 1991

Cat

C razy creature.
A dventurous cat on four legs.
T ired.

Ruby (7)
Chellaston Junior School, Chellaston

Who Loves Cats?

C ats are great
A nd are like a clean plate.
T he people say it's fluffy.
S o it's on its cutely made

A nd it's a button.
R ight is for cats, not left.
E ats fish, not cat food.

G reat cats are rare like ours.
R eally likes a clean plate.
E nergy is full for cats
A nd not for bats.
T he cat is... great!

Ibrahim Mahmood (8)
Dixons Marchbank Primary School, Bradford

Super Cat

There is a cat who likes to sit on the mat,
She has wings like a bat.
She flies higher and higher in the sky,
With her friends and family.
The one she hates she will not let them play.
She scratches them all night.
In the morning she goes to sleep
And sleeps like a dog.
She wakes up in the night
And goes to play with her friends
Like a good little cat.

Hibba Hassain (8)
Dixons Marchbank Primary School, Bradford

My Cat

Some cats are big and eat like a pig.
Some cats are small and are not tall.
Some cats are bold, they don't do what they are told.
Some cats are shy but they like to creep by.
Some cats are mean and should be seen.
Some cats are snappy, they make me unhappy.
Some cats are rough, I've had enough!
But my cat is sweet, she's the best cat to meet.

Tayyibah Munir (8)
Dixons Marchbank Primary School, Bradford

The New Dog, Maverick

M e and Maverick walked past the tree

A nd in the distance we saw the sea,

V ery calm and peaceful.

E very day we go for a walk.

R ed leaves fall down.

I f they fall autumn has arrived.

C old winter nights will take over.

K eep yourself safe, Covid is around.

Abdulaboor Hussain (8)

Dixons Marchbank Primary School, Bradford

Kitty Love

My little kitty is my best friend.
I love her so much till the very end.
She likes to cuddle with me and play,
She is the highlight of my day.
Sassy, adorable, fluffy and cute,
She needs a good night's sleep to reboot.
Her furry hair goes curly and twisty,
She is our favourite kitty called Misty.

Inaya Hussain (8)
Dixons Marchbank Primary School, Bradford

A Bright, Colourful Parrot

P ink, blue, red and green.

A n extraordinary parrot can be seen.

R adiant and majestic, she soars through the breeze.

R evealing her vibrant colours with ease.

O ver the oceans and under the sun.

T he most beautiful creature, having some fun.

Sehr Zafran (8)

Dixons Marchbank Primary School, Bradford

Charlie

C ome and see Charlie.

H e can't stay in warm countries.

A nt, I call him Ant.

R olls around the house.

L ies around and goes to sleep.

I n warm days he has a bath.

E saa, my little brother, he likes to play with.

Musa Mohammad (8)
Dixons Marchbank Primary School, Bradford

Tom And Pom

There was a man who bought a dog and a cat.
He named one Tom and the other one Pom.
Pom was ginger and so was Tom
Then they both got injured
So they set off for a journey one early afternoon.

Aayat Hussain (8)

Dixons Marchbank Primary School, Bradford

Our Puppies

The dogs run as quick as a blink
Their little ears are soft as silk
They're prettier than a flower
They like climbing towers.

Amina Ali (8)
Dixons Marchbank Primary School, Bradford

The Apocalypse Petunia

Far away in a distant land
There lives a creature with flamboyance
And the most lethal teeth of all.

It lives in snowy mountains,
Munches on wires
But is a deadly weapon.

It could live to up to 500 years old
But it shouldn't be fooled,
For it knows the most powerful magic of all.

It entertains the Eskimos,
With its solar-powered TV,
So you must be impressed.

It lives in groups called a Swarmbee
And they sometimes go on journeys to the Amazon
To visit their cousins, the Moonlight Disasters.

Akshadha Jacksun (11)
Lee Chapel Primary School, Basildon

The Piraniad

The Piraniad lives in sand and sea.
He can talk, swim and grant wishes.
He has a rivalry with the honey-giving bee
And can give you food on dishes.

He can swim faster than 60 miles per hour
And lives in holes in the sand,
His arms can swim with incredible power
And a strand of his whiskers fertilises the land.

He's a hybrid of the Psammead and piranha,
And is the wisest thing alive,
Nobody knows his owner,
Though I think his name is Clive.

Max Huggins (10)
Lee Chapel Primary School, Basildon

Crazy Cog-Topus

The cog-topus is not a normal animal,
It's a dog, an octopus and a cow.
It's not scared to bark at a cannibal,
Whenever somebody sees it, they say, "Wow!"

He's very timid
But very playful.
He can sometimes be rigid
But his only emotion is being joyful.

The cog-topus' tentacles are long
As it's what he uses to walk.
Not only agile but strong,
It causes everyone to gawk.

Lowalekar (10)
Lee Chapel Primary School, Basildon

The Acrobatic Rabbit

This acrobatic rabbit
Is not just a rabbit,
It does acrobatics
Which is kind of like gymnastics.

Its favourite colour is orange
Because he loves carrots
And they are the colour orange.

His name is Ben
And he is very tough,
When it comes to competitions
Because in the first completion
He wasn't smiling.

Faramade Aderin (10)
Lee Chapel Primary School, Basildon

Simba

I have a pet,
He is named Simba,
He is half-lion and half-shark,
He can crawl, he can dance,
He's tall, he's fast.

He's clumsy, he's naughty,
He's funny, he's silly,
He's young, he's annoying,
He's lazy, he's picky.

He's talented, he's smart
And he's mine.

Veera Pasapula (10)
Lee Chapel Primary School, Basildon

My Greedy Schnauzer

My greedy Schnauzer snuffles and squirms
As she runs around the garden hunting for worms.
She goes under bushes and all around the trees
While she hunts around and eats everything she sees.

Her tummy is fluffy and big and round
And she runs very fast to show what she has found.

My greedy Schnauzer has a pink glittery nose and sparkly ears.
When she wags her curly tail food magically appears.
When she sits down her feet turn out like a dancer,
Then she licks her lips and dreams of eating bananas.

My greedy Schnauzer loves eating and eating,
Then at the end of the day she just likes sleeping.

Elizabeth Costain (8)
Lenham Primary School, Lenham

Demon Dracula

My pet is Dracula.
He is a bit weird ya know.
Catching mice and birds is his thing.
Probably like every other cat on Earth
But my cat is an actual demon!
That might seem a bit odd but I'm not lying.
You see he isn't much of a human lover.
However, he seems nice at one time
But that time is breakfast time.
He has tried to bite me for no reason... multiple times!
When it gets dark he gets all playful
And pounces at people's feet
And it's like he goes into demon mode.
All you can see are his flashing green eyes when it's dark...
Anyway, that's why my cat is a demon!

Jessica Cushion (9)
Lenham Primary School, Lenham

The Unicorn Cat

There once was a cat called Bow
Who met a friend, no foe,
The cute friend was a unicorn,
With a marvellous rainbow horn.

The cat and the unicorn were ever so cute,
They danced around, playing the flute,
The marvellous two danced as one,
The cat and the unicorn were having so much fun!

Under the stars, they started to shine,
Something magical started to pine...
The unicorn and the cat danced so great,
They really were the best of mates.

Then was born the unicorn-cat,
She was so agile like a bat,
She was cute and so furry,
Her adorable fur was so curly!

Skye Jackson (8)
Lenham Primary School, Lenham

Reggie Roo

I have a dog called Reg,
He is not allowed in my bed.
He is fawn and blue
With a bit of black too.
Oh and by the way, he likes to eat his poo!
We call him Baby Shark
Although sharks can't bark.
He went for his first walk to the park
But all he did was eat bark.
He is very funny
And loves to bundle our house bunny.
He is my favourite pet
Unless he bites me, then he's not.
Reggie, I love you
But I still won't clean up your poo!

Millie Sharp (8)
Lenham Primary School, Lenham

My Cats

Cooper Trooper is my black and white cat.
Meow Meow is my favourite cat.
Josie Jump, she really jumps.
Ginger is really ginger.
Hamley is really lazy.
Chea looks like a cheetah and is really fast.
Veronique comes from France.
Little Miss Minnie Meow Meow is a mini Meow
Meow.
Tabby Cat has a pretty face.
These are all my favourite cats.

Isabella Young (8)
Lenham Primary School, Lenham

Goblin Gaston

Goblin Gaston...
It sounds like he gobbles up his food
But really he doesn't eat his breakfast.
I know it's weird.
When he does eat it
It ends up all over his mouth like a beard.
And then he was hungry
And that's what I feared.
His claws are sharp
And his paws need a bath
And I laugh when he barks.

Poppy Storey (8)
Lenham Primary School, Lenham

Gizmo The Lazy Cat

Gizmo is a lazy cat that likes to sit on furry mats.
Gizmo likes to sleep on my bed
And sometimes he sleeps on my head.
Gizmo likes to meow a lot for attention he has
already got.
Gizmo is my best friend,
If he was famous he would be on trend.

Riley Carrano (8)
Lenham Primary School, Lenham

Sassy Steven

I have a pet called Steven,
He is very round and even,
I gave him a pat,
But he was still sass,
I gave him a flute,
He gave it a toot,
I have a pet called Steven,
He is round and even.

Louanna Lambert (8)
Lenham Primary School, Lenham

The Astro DNA Cat

T he astro cat was me but I, Astro DNA Cat

H ave the best place to live, the

E xtraordinary science lab. We collect DNA from

A ll around the world. We get DNA from

S aturn, Jupiter and everywhere else.

T he best kind of DNA is from animals but we don't

R eally do animals, we do space.

O h did I say I've got a friend, Raven, who gets

D NA with me and he loves it as much as his

N anny which is really nice. She gives us

A ll the treats she has in the world.

C ats are best. We all love treats, especially cats.

A ll cats like Dreamies treats, what cats don't?

T he DNA is the best type, we select from planets and make new ones.

James Casey (9)
Litcham School, Litcham

The Lanky Ladybug

There was a lanky ladybug
Who snuck around at night
Snatching, stealing, taking stuff
From bugs all around town.

"This must stop," the bugs agreed
And so they hatch a plan
To stop this lanky ladybug
Who snuck around at night.

So one night when the ladybugs were asleep
The other bugs crept into his house
And caught him red-handed
in the sack that they brought.

"Help, oh no!" the ladybug cried.
"Don't worry," the other bugs said.
"We won't hurt you,
We just want you to stop."
"Stop what?" he said.
"The burgling you do."
"Oh okay, I'll try."
"Oh fabulous," the bugs cried.

And so the ladybug
Never did anything bad again.

Ivo Pickard (9)
Litcham School, Litcham

Doog! The Dog On The Speaker

There is a dog who lives on a speaker.
There is a bed for the dog on the speaker.
The speaker is big and grand,
Soon it will come down with a splat!
The speaker is breaking.
The speaker is waking.
The speaker is shaking.
The speaker is cold.
The speaker is dull.
The speaker is bland.
It's like a snail breaking as slow as a slug, poor
Doog.
Doog the dog is a walking pillow, he is so soft.
The speaker is crying, it's falling.
One day it will be like when it began,
We need a handyman,
We need a saviour to fix us up.
We need to make it like when it started.

The dog on the speaker is called Doog.
His future awaits on his little speaker.
For this little creature called Doog,
The dog on the speaker.

Tristan How (10)

Litcham School, Litcham

Cranky Capybara

Capybara can't swim.
Capybara isn't kind.
Capybara wrecks everything.
He killed all the Queen's knights
And broke all the street's lights.

This capybara has long sharp claws
That he uses to break down doors.
He escaped from the zoo many moons ago.
He ran across the rooftops, his body curving low.

He's as bulky as a car
And as fat as a log.
He goes along eating other people's dogs.
He likes to throw things on the floor,
Always ready to break the law.
He lives with me.
He came here last night.
I'm now teaching him not to bite.

Capybara can swim.
Capybara is kind.

Capybara has fixed everything
And helped all the Queen's knights.

Tegan Smith (9)
Litcham School, Litcham

Spider Cat

There's a cat next door who breaks the law.
He's known as, drum roll please, Spider Cat!
He is dodging, daring and dangerous.
He has a habit of playing with my rabbit!
Spider Cat wears a hat,
Eats rats and bats on my mat,
But that's not all...
He throws his ball in the pool.
Next thing you know, *splash!*
Your house is flooded.

At night he's in the sky, flying high
And shooting a web at my auntie Deb, "Argh!"
He's falling through the air.
I drop my pear and, to my despair,
I catch Spider Cat and his black hollow hat.
He's a dodging, daring, dangerous ball of fluff.

Reece Watts (10)
Litcham School, Litcham

The Night Ruler

A regular human you think?
Well, think again.
No face on its head
But on the chest eight eyes
And no time wasted.

From web to web
He takes the things
And out the window he is led.
With nothing left
But an 'argh' from the robbed people of the house.

What is this creature you ask?
I call it The Night Ruler
Or TNR for short.

When the moon is high
It's time to strike!
Yes, I'm here,
But not to fear
Because I'm not it
And I'm out of here
But was it a dream?

Raphael Westwood (9)
Litcham School, Litcham

Food Puppy

Food Puppy is no normal puppy,
For Food Puppy is a puppy that has a jetpack
And flies to hot dog stands.
McPuppy, here it comes,
It is a bird?
Is it a plane?
It's a fantastic flying food puppy, argh!
With a zoom and a whoosh, all the food gone.
The furry UFO is whizzing past you,
It's like a jet with three million miles per hour
rocket boosters.
No food is safe from this mad puppy.
When it flies past you it whooshes at you
And all the food will be stolen
And when it comes back home you know dinner is
served!

James Millward (9)
Litcham School, Litcham

Cat Of The Night

C at of the year,

A marvellous love to me.

T o a criminal she is their most dangerous nightmare.

O n her extraordinary palace of clouds she lies.

F or she is a dangerous angel of the night.

T he cat knows

H ow to be sassy and fight.

E nergy in her claws.

N o one defeats the cat of the night.

I am her most clever and marvellous friend.

G o on and be victorious like her!

H armony is her love.

T obby she is.

Lyra Bannister (9)
Litcham School, Litcham

The Super Dog

T oday Super Dog has a busy day.
H e will accomplish his goal to save the world.
E arth needs his super marvellous power.

S uper Dog will sacrifice the meanies.
U p, up and away.
P repare for the world to be saved.
E very superpower activated.
R eady steady go, *boom, pow, crash, bang, thud!*

D angerous, extraordinary, incredible Super Dog.
O MG! He achieved his goal to save the world.
G reat job, extraordinary work Super Dog.

Caden Brabant (10)
Litcham School, Litcham

Slapdog Was Born

S lapdog is super special.

L ike a mother she cares for ten puppies.

A fter being a glowing blue egg and growing into a

P latypus months later it grew a

D og's head and body then a

O tter's tail, the tail was bigger than her.

G ood girl for not barking.

I s that you playing at barking?

S top barking, now!

G o, go, go, go!

O h what a good girl.

O h did you poop on the floor?

D o clean it up!

Damian Rees (9)

Litcham School, Litcham

Jimmy The Mind-Reading Dog

Jimmy the mind-reading dog,
Smart, intelligent and secretive.
Striding in the streets of Manchester
With his black top hat, his white bow tie
And his dark navy suit.

Looking in people's fascinating minds,
Woof! he said to the man.
The man was upset, frustrated and angry.
Jimmy talked to him.
He suggested options to make him feel better.

The man thanked him.
He was as happy as an Olympic gold medalist.
Jimmy the mind-reading dog,
Another case solved.

May Pick (9)
Litcham School, Litcham

Catpurrd

There is a bird called Catpurrd and it is scared to
fly.
She always lies when she vlogs on her brilliant
blog.
She always says goodbye
When the others fly.

She's scared, she's colourful and marvellous to see.
She always makes you feel glee,
But don't think she is easy to spot,
She is tiny, like a dot.

She's extraordinary and marvellous to see.
She is small like a bee
And hard to see.
But always makes you feel glee.

Katherine Seales (9)
Litcham School, Litcham

The Detective Dog

Detective Dog loves solving crimes,
He runs and jumps and up the wall he climbs!
But in the daytime he's a normal dog,
So cute and cuddly and brown like a log.
When the clock strikes midnight...
He gets ready to fight!
He grabs his hat,
And in a flash, he's over the doormat.
He needs to get home soon,
A disappearing moon!
A rising sun,
Get back to Mum!
On the floor he lands,
Back in nice warm hands.

Erin Reynolds (9)
Litcham School, Litcham

Sweety, The Holiday Cat

Your cats are probably sleepy and sneaky.
Sweety is different.
She travels to Spain and she is tamed.
She likes to have a smoothie with her friend, Sussy.
Sweety likes to swim in a shallow lake
Because it feels like she is going to bake.
Ring, ring! Her phone rings,
It is time to go or else your mother will hear.
She gets on the plane to fly away from Spain
Now she is home and being quite lazy.

Martha Wright (9)
Litcham School, Litcham

My Cat In The Hat

I have a cat in a black top hat.
He is as fluffy as a huge fat mat.
He likes to get patted on his big black hat.

I play with my cat in the big black hat.
We normally play 'what's that cat in the big black hat?'

When it's night-time we snuggle in bed
And I always say,
"I love my cat in the big black hat!"

Faris Matsell (9)
Litcham School, Litcham

Secret Life Of Snoball

S noball the bunny, sweet and cute,

N obody has a bunny like Snoball.

O nly Snoball can fight like a lion.

B ad guys beware of Snoball.

A mazing Snoball bursts from walls like a wrecking ball.

L isten up, don't be bad or Snoball will get mad.

L isten, be good and the fighting machine will stay happy.

Ollie Barron (9)
Litcham School, Litcham

Samy The Singing Seahorse

Sammy was a strange seahorse.
In the day he was fine.
At night he sang his scales off, blowing his mind.
Everyone loved his sweet singing.
It put them to sleep like a lullaby.
His glorious, smooth song was like silk.
He roared the night away with a neigh.
In the day he rested.
Well done, Sammy, the singing seahorse.

Philippa Elburn (9)
Litcham School, Litcham

My Snake

Look at my snake it can bake a cake
It can even make a steak! It can fry
It can bake you a pie!
It will hiss, it can fry
And it can even fly!
It's thinner than air!
It is really long
And it really likes to play
Ping pong!
But also be cautious
Because this snake that can fly can also
Spy!

Katie Hanson
Litcham School, Litcham

Elfdog

E xcellent at eating
L oud for humming
F luff for me to be warm
D oggy animal
O bvious to see
G ood at races.

Georgia Moores (9)

Litcham School, Litcham

My Pet Hyde

Every day after school,
My pet, Hyde is at the door,
Leaping up and down in excitement,
Like a newborn puppy
For he's my best buddy.

Every day a new place,
Sometimes so pretty, I do nothing but gaze,
We go on amazing adventures,
Sometimes back to another date,
For he's my best mate.

Colourful scales he has,
But when he lets out gas
It's best to hold your nose,
To each other, private letters we send
For he's my best friend.

He climbs, swims and runs faster than me,
But I don't really mind, you see,
We both love each other very much
And I never want to see him go,
For he's my BFF.

Louisa Hardovin-Munro (10)

Melrose At The Ladies College, St Peter Port

Bolt The Wonder Dog

His name is Bolt,
He's purple and bright.
He likes wearing colour and that's alright.
His owner called Mark lives on the edge of Sark.
The two are inseparable, buddies forever!

But blazing Bolt is always rushing away
To help others and save the day.

Put others first, he heard one day,
"But what about Mark?" he dared to say.
What about the ups and downs they had,
The laughs, the cries, it wasn't so bad.

They did it together hand in paw,
And that's all that matters,
Best buddies for evermore!

So brilliant Bolt went back
And didn't lack, the confidence to say,
"Marvellous Mark, I missed you, please may I
stay?"

Mark replied as happy as can be,
"Of course dear buddy, I only wanted you and me!"

So since then life was a dream
They were helping others, the amazing dream team!

Rea Moore (10)
Melrose At The Ladies College, St Peter Port

Beware The Snortous

Never go to the town,
Never go to my street.
Never go to my house,
For some people have a nice little mouse, I don't.
No bunny. No cat. Drat!
I don't have that. I have a snortous.

A tortoise by day, no doubt about that,
But by night even the dogs scat.

Terrible teeth, wrinkly skin,
It's a wonder he keeps his meanness in, almost.
Go near him, you're toast.
One more thing you have to know...
His nose is as long as a garden hose.

Alexa Stockwell (10)
Melrose At The Ladies College, St Peter Port

The Marvellous Squigeon

I am a squirrel but also a pigeon,
Therefore I'm known as the marvellous squigeon.
I love a few breadcrumbs with a side of nuts,
I open their shells and I pull out their guts.
I have three little legs and only one wing,
Which makes me unique and a beautiful thing.
I pester for food but I run away too,
Especially from humans as large as you!

Holly Jones (10)
Melrose At The Ladies College, St Peter Port

Bunnies

B eautiful
U nexpected
N aturalist
N aughty
Y outhful.

Beautiful bunnies...
All about saving people's lives by jumping about.
If you see them you know what to do.
Shout, "Bunnies!"
And they will come to you!

Amelia Willis (10)
Melrose At The Ladies College, St Peter Port

The Acrosage

A crobatic.

C lever.

R adiant.

O bedient.

S ausage eating.

A dorable.

G orgeous.

E xtraordinary sausage dog.

Caitlin Vidamour (10)
Melrose At The Ladies College, St Peter Port

Cats

C ute and lazy
A re cats.
T iny and tame,
S assy and amazing.

Isabelle Guest (10)

Melrose At The Ladies College, St Peter Port

Shark World

F lying high in the sky or
L ying low beneath the sea,
Y awning at the end of day.
I n the ocean he is free.
N o one scares him at the beach,
G oing solo on his way.

O nto bigger, brighter things,
C alling friends along the way.
T angled tentacles everywhere.
O bedient and gentle beast.
P ushing vigorously through the waves.
U sing his wings to propel him into the air.
S harp, shiny scissor-shaped teeth.

S parkling in the sunlight.
H igh above the world,
A iring his wings,
R aking through the wind,
K illing time.

Cayde Cummins (7)
St Andrew's CE Primary School, Plymouth

My Tiny Giraffe

My tiny giraffe is as small as my nail,
My tiny giraffe is as slow as a snail.
My tiny giraffe is as yellow as a flower,
My tiny giraffe has got lots of power.
My tiny giraffe is extremely soft,
My tiny giraffe hides up in the loft.
My tiny giraffe eats dandelion leaves,
My tiny giraffe has a coat with sleeves.
My tiny giraffe gets stuck in a tree,
My tiny giraffe gets rescued by a bee.
My tiny giraffe has a leafy bed,
My tiny giraffe goes there to rest his head.
My tiny giraffe is a bit magical,
My tiny giraffe is entirely fanciful!

Tabitha Ryder (7)
St Andrew's CE Primary School, Plymouth

Bunny Land

Cute, fluffy bunnies, love their carrots.
They like chasing lots of parrots.
Some fall asleep in their cosy bushes,
They love a good night sleep.
Come in, it's the morning, it's time to wake up.
They run around the field having such a great time.
Today there's lots of birds tweeting all the time.
Now it's dinnertime, they eat lots of their dinner.
Come on, it's time to play a little tag game.
After the game it's time to have a long drink.
Now it's time for bed, we'll see you in the morning.

Molly Pinder (8)
St Andrew's CE Primary School, Plymouth

My Dog

My dog is marvellous
And friendly with my friends.
Sometimes can be messy
But I love him so much.
Sometimes he is clumsy and gentle and ruffly.
He bites and chews clothes.
I throw him in the air.
He lets people stroke him.
He is incredible with his tricks and can roll over
And creeps up to scare my friends.
He jumps high in the air.
He cries all the time when I leave.
He is lazy and sleepy.
He likes me to scratch his belly.

George Andrei (8)
St Andrew's CE Primary School, Plymouth

Polly, The Marvellous Dog

Polly started like a normal dog
Until she licked a magic frog.
Her wings started to grow a bit
But Polly didn't notice it.
When Polly went for a walk one crispy eve
People, they could not believe...
Polly was flying, chasing a bee,
All the way around a Christmas tree.
The flying continued with a whizz, bang and a pop.
Suddenly one day the flying began to stop.
Back to normal for this cute dog,
After licking the magic frog!

Iyla Hammond (8)
St Andrew's CE Primary School, Plymouth

The Scared Pet

I have a peculiar pet called Spiker.
He lives in a big room in my house.
He's clever, gentle and cool
But he's really scared of a mouse.
He likes to meet new people
And go for a walk in the park
But he hides a secret from people...
He's really scared of the dark.
I bought him in the mall
Where they told me there's nothing he likes better
Than to play with his rainbow bouncy ball!

Noah Wallbridge-Willcocks (8)
St Andrew's CE Primary School, Plymouth

No Clue

No Clue is his name,
He may not be for you,
He's shiny and bright,
He'll cheer you up,
With his ten marvellous legs
He'll outrun you.

We often wonder why he has two heads
Which leaves us with no clue!
He's clever and cheeky
And will trick you with his smooth moves.

I love my No Clue,
Without him I would be blue,
Without a clue what to do!

Freddie Colling (7)
St Andrew's CE Primary School, Plymouth

My Imaginary Flying Dog

M arvellously mad.
Y apping all the time.

F lying fast in the air.
L aughing loudly as he goes.
Y elling when he doesn't get his way.
I n the air, flying high.
N ever giving up on fun.
G reeting everyone he meets.

D oesn't mean any harm.
O ur one of a kind hero.
G entle all the way.

Catherine Phillips Ebohon (7)
St Andrew's CE Primary School, Plymouth

Cute Cat

C ute Cat is a colourful chameleon.

U ndercover is his job as Spy Cat.

T rendy disguises are his secret speciality. He has

E xtraordinary powers like changing colour.

C lever, courageous and as cute as a newborn kitten.

A crobatics are his game as he cartwheels across the floor.

T wisting and turning, stretching his paws like rubber bands!

Yohan Dean (7)
St Andrew's CE Primary School, Plymouth

Crazy Coco

My crazy canine, Coco
Is just a little bit loco.
She's a juggling, unicycling trumpet-playing dog!
If you go to the park today
You're bound to see her on the way,
Sat on her saddle with three juggling balls
And on her way to the mall.
Coco gets home and it's been a busy day.
It's time for a nap now.
Be quiet everyone or else you will get a snap!

Emily-Rose Trevaskus
St Andrew's CE Primary School, Plymouth

Fire Dino Cat

F erocious little cat with
I ncredibly
R azor-sharp claws.
E nergetically runs fast around town.

D angerous fire from her
I mpeccable horns, she is
N osy with a beautiful
O range glow.

C ute, fluffy cat with
A dorable eyes, don't be fooled, she is as
T ame as can be.

Amber Loram-Martin (7)
St Andrew's CE Primary School, Plymouth

My Pet Narwhal

My pet narwhal is a bit different.

My pet narwhal has two sparkly horns.

My pet narwhal is my shiny, spotty friend.

My pet narwhal lets me ride on her back.

My pet narwhal takes me to an enchanted place.

My pet narwhal meets her family and we explore together.

My pet narwhal takes me home to bed after a busy day.

Orla Stafford (7)
St Andrew's CE Primary School, Plymouth

The One And Only Mo Fisher

I am Mo Fisher,
I'm smooth and I'm slick.
When it comes to gold medals,
I don't miss a trick.
My teeth are sharp,
My legs are strong,
With a flick of my tail
To speed me along.
I can see the finish,
I can cross the line.
Bronze, silver, gold,
The world record is mine!

Jacqueson Berry (7)
St Andrew's CE Primary School, Plymouth

Sophisticated, Scared Bruce The Budgie

Bruce is annoying and loud.
He's as blue as the sky
And as white as a cloud.
He makes a horrible sound
And likes to move his seeds all around.
We let him fly
And he lands on my head when he gets up high.
I love him to bits, my wonderful Bruce,
But really he is just a nincompoop!

Delphine Marie Edwards (7)
St Andrew's CE Primary School, Plymouth

My Pet, Rex

Colossal and green.
Incredible spikes.
Sharp claws and teeth
But he won't bite!
He loves to skateboard in the sun.
With me on my bike
We have such fun
Until it's time for tea.
We wonder... what will it be?
My funny pet, Rex,
He's a dinosaur, you see!

Theo Strong (7)
St Andrew's CE Primary School, Plymouth

Poem For My Cat

My cat is as beautiful as a house,
Both quarrelsome and soft.
Mum and Dad didn't want to take it
Until they discovered the value,
The value of this cat.
It's great because she's my cat
And she's the best friend on the planet.

Daria Bighiu (7)
St Andrew's CE Primary School, Plymouth

Ladybug

R iley the ladybug really is tiny.

I n the garden she slimes and is very slimy.

L adybug Riley really wants to fly.

E sa the butterflly helps him reach the sky.

Y ou cannot tell anyone that Riley is very shy.

Rehaan Chatterjee (7)

St Andrew's CE Primary School, Plymouth

About My Peculiar Pet

Adorable is my pet's power
And it is super-duper agile.
My pet is extra marvellous.
Being protective is my pet's duty.
Playful is the mood that my pet is always in
And is always in a good mood.

Nathan Ogwu (8)
St Andrew's CE Primary School, Plymouth

My Cat, Bubbles

I have a cat called Bubbles
Who likes lots of cuddles.
He likes to sit on my lap
And have a nap.
He has purple fur and likes to purr.
He's my colourful, extraordinary, marvellous purple
cat.

Mia Flynn (8)
St Andrew's CE Primary School, Plymouth

My Cat

M y cat is the best in the world.
Y ay, she's so soft!

C uteness and cuddling is her thing.
A t places she stays nearby.
T he best cat in the world is mine.

Audrey Victoria Almirante Biggs (7)
St Andrew's CE Primary School, Plymouth

Famous Frank

F rank is famous.

R eally it is true!

A ruffle and a snuffle is what he likes to do.

N ow it's time for a nap.

K eep quiet everyone else you'll get a snap.

Florence Caroline Cronin (7)
St Andrew's CE Primary School, Plymouth

Kiny Winy Winsy The Furious

Kiny Winy Winsy is my weird cat
Who is a little bit fat.
His whiskers are long,
He looks like King Kong,
He is so adorable
I love him.
He is messy
But he is my bestie!

Tatiana Terzakis (7)
St Andrew's CE Primary School, Plymouth

Snowflake

S nowy

N avigator

O pening doors

W eird

F unny

L aughing

A lways nice

K ind

E xtraordinary.

Leela Peacock (7)
St Andrew's CE Primary School, Plymouth

Drama Llama

Penguin Llama loves lots of drama.
The funny thing is he believes in karma.
His furry hair means he doesn't care
But he is adorable and sassy so no one cares.

Hugo Chester (7)
St Andrew's CE Primary School, Plymouth

Ferocious Dragon

D angerous dragon.

R oaring loudly.

A mazingly eating trees.

G iant mouth.

O pening claws.

N aughty behaviour.

Wojtek Waloszczyk (8)
St Andrew's CE Primary School, Plymouth

YoungWriters®
Est. 1991

YOUNG wRITERS INFORMATION

We hope you have enjoyed reading this book – and that you will continue to in the coming years.

If you're a young writer who enjoys reading and creative writing, or the parent of an enthusiastic poet or story writer, do visit our website **www.youngwriters.co.uk**. Here you will find free competitions, workshops and games, as well as recommended reads, a poetry glossary and our blog. There's lots to keep budding writers motivated to write!

If you would like to order further copies of this book, or any of our other titles, then please give us a call or order via your online account.

Young Writers
Remus House
Coltsfoot Drive
Peterborough
PE2 9BF
(01733) 890066
info@youngwriters.co.uk

Join in the conversation!
Tips, news, giveaways and much more!

 YoungWritersUK    @YoungWritersCW